CW00393621

Rowan Waller is an entrepreneur, business owner and author who lives in Oxford, England,
with his wife Jenny and their two daughters.

"Being an entrepreneur isn't about becoming rich. It is *certainly* not about becoming rich to the
detriment of others. It is about taking responsibility for your own destiny, spotting opportunities and
seizing them, and learning to think differently about risk and reward. It is about aspiring to do good for
yourself and your family (which should be something to celebrate, not to be embarrassed about) and,
most of all in my view, it is also about creating for yourself a chance to give back and do some good…
to do good in your community, town, city or county, to help out with or even to lead good causes
and – if you really make it – it should become a chance to do good on a global scale.
This to me has always been the essence of the entrepreneur."

"This one is for Leila and Pippa, my own two little entrepreneurs."

ROWAN WALLER

Published in 2021

Published in the UK by Ink Spot Books
An imprint of Ink Spot Books Ltd. 33 Aldrich Road, Oxford, OX2 7SS UK
www.inkspotbooks.net

ISBN 978-1-91961-892-0

Written by Rowan Waller
Illustrated by T G H Robins

BILLY THE GOAT
AND THE FIVE POUND NOTE

This isn't the story of Old Farmer Giles,

Whose family farm stretched miles and miles.

This is the story of Billy the Goat,

And the day that he found a five pound note.

Counting his cash up, one winter's day,

Giles knew that a fiver had fluttered away.

An icy gust snatched it straight out of his hand

And carried it off; now, where would it land?

He watched as it dropped in the hay in the yard,

Just as his Billy-Goat chomped down hard.

He saw Billy spit it out onto the floor,

And he scoffed: "Keep it, goat – I've got plenty more!"

Well, Billy just couldn't believe his eyes:

"Five Pounds of my own!? Now, what shall I buy!?

Five bags of carrots? A pallet of fruit?

A pedicure treat for my cloven hooves?"

"Top Yacht Magazine (well, a goat's gotta dream),

Or a Bus Trip to London to wave at the Queen!

I can only pick one, so I'd better get picking…

Or maybe, just maybe…" – and his brain started ticking…

That night when Billy went back to his pen,

He said to the sheep and the pig and the hen:

"There's a pound for you each and a bed of fresh hay,

If you'll come to work with me for a day."

Next morning he went to see David the Printer,

Who was grateful for work in the middle of winter.

"I've got a new Petting Zoo, entry's a quid."

"I print signs for two bob," said Dave - and he did!

That afternoon Billy led out his mates,

And set up his sign outside the school gates.

They waited, and then at kicking-out time,

Five kids and their parents had soon formed a line.

That night, when Billy was back in his pen,

He mused how his five pound note was now ten,

And he said to the hen and the sheep and the pig:

"Let's go back tomorrow; this could be big…"

Now five pounds in profit, he went back to see Dave.

"This needs to be something the public will crave."

Dave thought for a moment: "If you want exposure,

Let's print up some leaflets and maybe a poster!"

By mid-afternoon, with exposure aplenty,

Yesterday's tenner had soon become twenty;

And by the end of the day – and here it gets nifty –

What began as a fiver was now a crisp fifty.

That night, to the pig and the hen and the sheep,

Billy said: "Thank you team. Now I'm taking a leap!

Here is a pay rise for all three of you,

As I want you to take over running the Zoo."

By the very next evening, from what had begun

As a soggy old fiver had now made a ton.

With his Petting Zoo managed, Billy was able

To next set his sights on Old Farmer Giles' stable.

"Let me lease this from you, Giles – ten bob a day,

Or a hundred a week with the nags and the hay."

Old Giles thought him simple, but what Billy planned

Were horse rides. That week he made his first grand.

When Springtime arrived, to the sheep, pig and hen,

Billy said: "Why don't we repeat this again?

"Each of you knows how to manage a Zoo,

So let's open another – in fact, make that two!"

At the stable, manure was forming in piles;

Billy stuck it in bags and sold it to Giles.

The bees in the eaves started churning out honey;

Billy stuck that in jars (and yes, made some money!).

Summer arrived and the Enterprise thrived!

More Zoos, more stables, more bees in the hive…

Billy opened a shop, selling honey and wax,

Taking orders online… and by phone… and by fax!

By the time Autumn came he had doubled again,

And promoted the sheep and the pig and the hen

To direct operations – and this will amaze ya –

In Europe, America – even in Asia!

Then back round to winter, a year and a day

Since finding five pounds in a mouthful of hay;

But who knew back then, who would ever have wondered,

That in just twelve months he'd be FTSE 100!?

Now it's easy to think being 'wealthy' means 'greedy',

But good goats like Billy do help out the needy;

So there's nothing wrong about making some money,

It's using it badly that's not very funny.

Billy for instance went out of his way

To invest in good causes, and later could pay

For a school, then a hospital, then the creation

Of his very own: 'The Billy Foundation'.

So that is the story of Billy the Goat,

And the way that he looked at his five pound note.

The five became ten, the ten became twenty,

Then fifty, a hundred, a thousand, which meant he

Could build up and expand, invest and aspire,

Diversify, merge, take over, acquire…

Billy started with little but now has a lot,

And he runs the whole thing from the deck of his yacht.

MANAGING DIRECTOR — FARMER GILES

Now, I know that you think that this story is silly.

So did Old Farmer Giles; now he's working for Billy…